IRISH
PUB
SONGS

SELECTED BY
GARETH JAMES

First published and printed by
The Appletree Press Ltd
7 James Street South
Belfast BT2 8DL
1983

ISBN 0 86281 015 9

Contents

Acknowledgements

For permission to reprint copyright material the
following acknowledgements are made:

For *Dan O'Hara*, to Walton's Musical Instrument
Galleries Ltd.; for *Don't Call Me Early in the
Morning* to Tommy Sands and Ellen Grove Music;
for *The Molly Maguires* to Mews Music Ltd; for *The
Spanish Lady* and *The Star of the Co. Down* to
Boosey and Hawkes Music Publishers Ltd.; for *The
Water Supply* to Eddie Callaghan; for *The Great
Shipyard Protest Parade* to Arnie Gardiner; for
Fiddler's Green to March Music.

The Cliffs of Dooneen

You- may tra-vel far far from your own na- tive home- Far a- way o'er the mountains a- way o'er the foam- But of all the fine pla-ces that I've e-ver been- sure there's none- to com-pare with the Cliffs of Doon-een-

It's a nice place to be on a fine summer's day
Watching all the wild flowers that ne'er do decay,
Oh, the hare and lofty pheasants are plain to be seen,
Making homes for their young on the Cliffs of Dooneen.

Take a view o'er the mountains, fine sights you'll see there,
You'll see the high rocky mountains on the west coast of Clare,
Oh, the towns of Kilkee and Kilrush can be seen
From the high rocky slopes of the Cliffs of Dooneen.

Fare thee well to Dooneen, fare thee well for a while,
And to all the fine people I'm leaving behind,
To the streams and the meadows where late I have been
And the high rocky slopes of the Cliffs of Dooneen.

As I Roved Out

Capo 5th Am

As I roved out on a May mor- ning, On a
May mor- ning right ear- ly, I met my love a-
long the way, Oh– Lord but she was ear- ly–

Chorus:

And she sang lilt a doo- dle lilt a doo- dle,
lilt a doo- dle dee and she hi- da- lan- da dee and she
hi- da- lan- da- dee and she lan- day–

Her boots were black and her stockings white,
And her buckles shone like silver,
And she had a dark and a rolling eye,
And her earrings tipped her shoulder.

Chorus

'What age are you, my nice sweet girl?
What age are you my honey?'
How modestly she answered me,
'I'll be sixteen age on Sunday.'

Chorus

I went to the house on the top of the hill
When the moon was shining clearly;
She arose to let me in,
For her mammy chanced to hear her.

Chorus

She caught her by the hair of the head,
And down to the room she brought her;
And with the root of a hazel twig,
She was the well-beat daughter.

Chorus

'Will you marry me now, my soldier lad?
Marry me now or never?
Will you marry me now, my soldier lad,
For you see I'm done forever?'

Chorus

'No, I won't marry you, my bonny wee girl,
I won't marry you, my honey,
For I have got a wife at home,
And how could I disown her?'

Chorus

A pint at night is my delight,
And a gallon in the morning;
The old women are my heartbreak,
But the young one is my darling.

Chorus

The Star of the County Down

Capo 3rd

Near to Banbridge town in the County Down One—morning in July, Down a boreen green came a sweet colleen And she smiled as she passed me by. Oh, she looked so neat from her two white feet to the sheen of her nut brown hair. Sure the coaxing elf, I'd to shake myself, To make sure I was standing there.

Oh, from Bantry Bay up to Derry Quay and from Galway to Dublin town, No— maid I've seen like the brown colleen that I met in the County Down.

Chorus

As she onward sped I shook my head,
And I gazed with a feeling quare,
And I said, says I, to a passer-by,
'Who's the maid with the nut-brown hair?'
Oh, he smiled at me, and with pride says he,
'That's the gem of Ireland's crown,
She's young Rosie McCann from the banks of the Bann,
She's the Star of the County Down.'

Chorus

I've travelled a bit, but never was hit
Since my roving career began;
But fair and square I surrendered there
To the charms of young Rosie McCann.
With a heart to let and no tenant yet
Did I meet with in shawl or gown,
But in she went and I asked no rent
From the Star of the County Down.

Chorus

At the cross roads fair I'll be surely there
And I'll dress in my Sunday clothes,
And I'll try sheep's eyes, and deludhering cries
On the heart of the nut-brown Rose.

8

No pipe I'll smoke, no horse I'll yoke,
Though my plough with rust turns brown,
Till a smiling bride by my own fireside.
Sits the Star of the County Down.

Chorus

Goodbye Mursheen Durkin

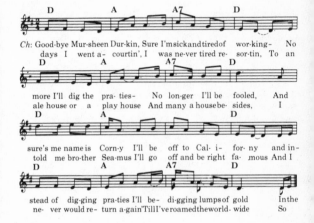

Ch: Good-bye Mur-sheen Dur-kin, Sure I'm sick and tired of wor-king- No
days I went a- courtin', I was ne-ver tired re- sor-tin, To an

more I'll dig the pra-ties- No lon-ger I'll be fooled, And
ale house or a play house And many a house be- sides, I

sure's me name is Corn-y I'll be off to Cal- i- for- ny and in-
told me bro-ther Sea-mus I'll go off and be right fa- mous And I

stead of dig-ging pra-ties I'll be- di-gging lumps of gold In the
ne- ver would re- turn a-gain Till I've roamed the world- wide So

O! I courted girls in Blarney,
In Kanturk and in Killarney,
In Passage and in Queenstown,
I mean the Cobh of Cork;
But I'm tired of all this pleasure,
So now I'll take my leisure,
And the next time that you hear from me,
'Twill be a letter from New York.

Chorus

© Appletree Press 1983

Botany Bay

I'm on my way down to the quay, where the ship at anchor lay,
To command a gang of navvies that they told me to engage,
I thought I would stop in for a while before I went away,
For to take that trip on an emigrant ship to the shores of Botany Bay.

Chorus

The boss came up this morning and he said to me, hello,
If you don't mix your mortar right, I'm afraid you'll have to go,
Well, since he did insult me, I demanded all my pay,
And I told him straight, I was going to emigrate to the shores of
  Botany Bay.

Chorus

And when I reach Australia, I'll go and dig for gold,
There's plenty there for the digging of, or so I have been told,
Or else I'll go back to my trade, and a hundred bricks I'll lay,
Before I've lived for an eight-hour shift on the shores of Botany Bay.

Chorus

The Black Velvet Band

Chorus:

Her eyes they shone like dia- monds, I thought her the Queen of the land And her hair hung o- ver her shoul- ders Tied up with a black vel-vet band~

As I went walking down Broadway,
Not intending to stay very long,
I met with a frolicsome damsel,
As she came a-tripping along,
She was both fair and handsome,
Her neck it was white as a swan,
And her hair hung over her shoulder,
Tied up with a black velvet band.

Chorus

I took a stroll with this pretty fair maid
When a gentleman passed us by,
I knew she had the taking of him
By the look in her roguish black eye.
A gold watch she took from his pocket
And put it right into my hand
On the very first day that I met her,
Bad luck to the black velvet band.

Chorus

Before judge and jury next morning
Both of us had to appear
The judge he said to me,'Young man,
Your case is proven clear.'
Seven long years' transportation,
Right on down to Van Dieman's Land
Far away from my friends and relations
Betrayed by the black velvet band.

Chorus

The Ould Woman from Wexford

The worm turns, and with what logic.

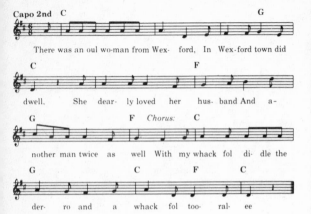

Capo 2nd

There was an oul wo-man from Wex- ford, In Wex-ford town did dwell. She dear- ly loved her hus- band And a- nother man twice as well With my whack fol di- dle the der- ro and a whack fol too- ral- ee

Ah, one day she went to a doctor
Some medicine for to find.
She said, 'Will you give me something
That'll make my old man blind?'

Chorus

Says he, 'Give him eggs and marrow bones
And make him sup them all,
And it won't be very long after
That he won't see you at all.'

Chorus

So she fed him eggs and marrow-bones,
And she made him sup them all,
And it wasn't so very long after
That he couldn't see the wall.

Chorus

Says th'old man, 'I think I'll drown myself,
But that might be a sin.'
Says she, 'I'll come along with you
And I'll help to shove you in.'

Chorus

Well, the old woman she stood back a bit
For to rush and push him in,
But the old man gently' stepped aside,
And she went tumblin' in.

Chorus

Oh, how loudly did she yell
And how loudly did she bawl
'Arra, hold your whist, y'old woman,
Sure I can't see you at all.'

Chorus

Ah, sure eggs are eggs and marrow-bones
Will make your old man blind,
But if you want to drown him,
You must creep up close behind.

Chorus

The Waxies' Dargle

Waxies were candlemakers, and dargles were their annual get-togethers.

Says my ould wan to your ould wan, sure we'll go to the Wax-ies' Dar-gle, Says your ould wan to my ould one, Sure I hav-en't got a far-thin'.

Chorus:

I just went down to Mon-to town to see young-Kill Mc-Ar-dle-sir- But he wouldn't give me a coup-le of bob To go to the Wax-ies' Dar-gle.

What'll you have? I'll have a pint, Yes I'll have a pint with you And if some-body does-n't or-der soon We'll be thrown out of the boo-zer.

Says my ould one to your ould one,
Will you come to the Galway Races,
Says your ould one to my ould one,
With the price of my ould lad's braces.
I went down to Capel Street,
To the Jew man money lenders
But they wouldn't give me a couple of bob
On my ould lad's red suspenders.

Chorus

Says my ould one to your ould one,
We have no beef or mutton
But if we go down to Monto Town
We might get a drink for nuthin'.
Here's a piece of advice I got
From an ould fishmonger
When food is scarce, and you see the hearse,
You'll know you've died of hunger.

Chorus

The Little Beggarman

♪. Unaccompanied

I am a lit- tle be-ggar-man a beg-ging I have been Aye for three score and ten- in this lit- tle isle of green And up- to the Lif- fey- down to Tess- a- gue And I'm known- by the name- of the Bold John-nie Dhu. Of all the trades a' go- in'- a- beg-ging is the best For when a man is tired- He can sit him down and rest. He begs- for his din-ner he has noth-ing else to do On- ly

D.s. al segno

1.2. 3.

cut a- round the cor-ner with his old rin- ga-do- I old rin-ga- do-

I slept last night in a barn at Curraghbawn,
A wet night came on and I skipped through the door,
Holes in my shoes and my toes peeping through,
Singin' skiddy-me-re-doodlum, for old Johnny Dhu.

I must be gettin' home for it's gettin' late at night,
The fire's all raked and there isn't any light.
An' now you've heard me story of the ould rigadoo,
It's goodnight and God bless you from ould Johnny Dhu.

Lannigan's Ball

In the town— of Athy, one Jer- e- my Lan- ni- gan,
gave a grand ball to his friends and re- la- tions,

Battered a- way till he had- n't a pound, His
Who did not for- get him when sent to the wall.

fa- ther he died and made him a man a- gain,
If you'd on-ly lis- ten I'll make your eyes glis- ten, At the

Left him a farm and ten a- cres of ground. He
rows and ruc- tions at Lan- ni- gan's ball.

Ch:
Six long months— I spent— in Du- blin,

Six long months do- ing, no-thing at all

Six long months— I spent— in Du- blin,

Learning the steps— for Lan- ni- gan's Ball.

Myself, to be sure, got free invitation
For all the nice boys an' girls that I'd ask,
In less than a minute the friends and relations
Were dancing as merry as bees round a cask.
Miss O'Hara, the nice little milliner,
Tipp'd me a wink to give her a call,
And soon we arrived with Timothy Galligan,
Just in time for Lannigan's Ball.

Chorus

They were doing all kinds of nonsensical polkas
All round the room in a neat whirligig;
But Julia and me soon banished nonsense
And tipp'd them a twist of a real Irish jig.

Och Mavrone, 'twas she that was glad o' me,
And danced till you'd think the ould ceiling would fall;
For I spent a whole fortnight at Burke's Academy,
Larnin' a step for Lannigan's Ball.

Chorus

The boys were all merry, the girls were all hearty,
Dancing away in couples and groups,
Till an accident happened young Terence McCarthy,
He put his right leg on Miss Flaherty's hoops,
The creature she fainted—roared milia murder,
Called for her friends and gathered them all,
Ned Carmody swore that he'd go no further,
But he'd have satisfaction at Lannigan's Ball.

Chorus

In the midst of the row Miss Kerrigan fainted,
Her cheeks all the while being red as a rose,
Some of the ladies declared she was painted,
She took a small drop too much, I suppose.
Her sweetheart, Ned Morgan, so powerful and able,
When he saw his fair colleen stretched by the wall,
He tore the leg from under the table,
And smashed all the chaney at Lannigan's Ball.

Chorus

Oh, boys, there was a ruction,
Myself got a kick from big Phelim McCue,
But soon I replied to this kind introduction,
And I kicked up a terrible Phillabooloo;
Ould Casey the piper was near being strangled,
They squeezed up his pipes, bellows, chanters and all;
The girls in their ribbons were all entangled,
And that put an end to Lannigan's Ball.

Chorus

O'Donnell Abu

Proud- ly the note of the trum- pet is soun- ding-
Loud- ly the war cries a- rise on the gale,
Fleet- ly the steed by Lough Swil- ly is boun- ding To
join the thick squa-d- rons in Sai- mear's green vale.
On ever- y mountain- eer, Stran- gers to fight and fear;
Rush to the stan-dard– of daunt- less Red Hugh!
Bon- naught and Gal- low-glass, Throng from each Mountain Pass-
on for old E- rin O' Don- nell A- bu.

Princely O'Neill to our aid is advancing,
With many a chieftain and warrior clan;
A thousand proud steeds in his vanguard are prancing,
'Neath the borderers brave from the banks of the Bann.
Many a heart shall quail
Under its coat of mail;
Deeply the merciless foeman shall rue
When on his ear shall ring
Borne on the breezes wing
Tir Connaill's dread war-cry—O'Donnell Abu!

Wildly o'er Desmond the war-wolf is howling,
Fearless the eagle sweeps over the plain,
The fox in the streets of the city is prowling—
All, all who would scare them are banished or slain!
Grasp every stalwart hand,
Hacbut and battle-brand—
Pay them all back the deep debt so long due:
Norris and Clifford well
Can of Tir Connaill tell—
Onward to glory—O'Donnell Abu!

Sacred the cause that Clann-Conaill's defending—
The altars we kneel at and the homes of our sires,
Ruthless the ruin the foe is extending—
Midnight is red with the plunderers fires!
On with O'Donnell then,
Fight the old fight again.
Sons of Tir Conaill, all valiant and true!
Make the false Saxon feel
Erin's avenging steel!
Strike for your country—O'Donnell Abu!

The Lark in the Morning

The lark in the morning she rises from her nest— She goes
off— every morning with the dew all on— her breast, And
like the jolly plough boy she whistles and she sings— She goes
home— every evening with the dew all on her wings—

Oh, Roger the ploughboy, he is a dashing blade,
He goes whistling and sighing over younder green glade,
He met with pretty Susan, she's handsome I declare,
She is far more enticing than the birds all in the air.

Chorus

One evening coming home from the rakes of the town,
The meadows being all green and the grass it being cut down,
If I should chance to tumble all in the new mown hay,
Oh, it's kiss me now or never, love, this bonny lass did say.

Chorus

When twenty long weeks they were over and were past,
Her mammy chanced to notice she'd thickened round the waist,
It was the handsome ploughboy the maiden she did say,
For he caused me for to tumble all in the new-mown hay.

Chorus

Here's a health to young ploughboys, wherever you may be,
That likes to have a bonny lass a-sitting on his knee
With a jug of good strong porter, you'll whistle and you'll sing,
For a ploughboy is as happy as a prince or a king.

Chorus

The Curragh of Kildare

This area, south-west of Dublin, is better known for its springy uphill turf, which has produced many of the world's best racehorses.

The winter it is past
And the summer's come at last.
The birds they are singing in-the trees-
Their little hearts are glad, but-
mine is very sad
For my true love is far away from me.
Chorus: And-

straight I will repair to the
Curragh of Kildare
For it's there I'll find
tidings of my dear.

The rose upon the briar by the water running clear
Brings joy to the linnet and the deer
Their little hearts are blessed, but mine knows no rest
For my true love is absent from me.

Chorus

A livery I'll wear and I'll comb back my hair
And in velvet so green I will appear
And straight I will repair to the Curragh of Kildare
For it's there I'll find tidings of my dear.

O you that are in love, and cannot it remove
I pity the pain you do endure,
For experience lets me know that your hearts are full of woe
A woe that no mortal can cure.

Chorus

The Greenland Whale Fisheries

In eight-teen hund-red and sev-en-ty two On-
March the eight-eenth day We-hoist-ed our col-ours to the
top-of the mast And for Green-land sailed a-
way, brave-boys, And for Green-land sailed a-way

The look-out on the mainmast he stood
His spyglass in his hand,
'There's a whale, there's a whale, there's a whale-fish,' he cried,
'And he blows at every span, brave boys,
And he blows at every span.'

The captain stood on the quarter deck,
A spyglass in his eye.
'Overhaul, overhaul, let your jib sheets fall
And launch your boats to sea, brave boys,
And launch your boats to sea.'

The boats were lowered and the men put out,
The whale was full in view.
Resolved, resolved was each whale-man bold
For to steer where the whale-fish blew, brave boys,
For to steer where the whale-fish blew.

The harpoon struck and the line ran out.
The whale gave a flick of his tail,
The boat capsized and five brave men were drowned
And we did not catch that whale, brave boys,
And we did not catch that whale.

The losing of those five jolly men.
It grieved our captain sore,
But the losing of that fine sperm whale,
Oh, it grieved him ten time more, brave boys,
Oh, it grieved him ten times more.

'Up anchor now,' our captain he cried,
'For the winter stars do appear,
And it's time we left this cold country,
And for the homeland we did steer, brave boys,
And for the homeland we did steer.'·

Well Greenland is a barren land,
A land that bears no green,
Where there's ice and snow and the whale-fishes blow,
And the daylight's seldom seen, brave boys,
And the daylight's seldom seen.

The Rocky Road to Dublin

Unaccompanied

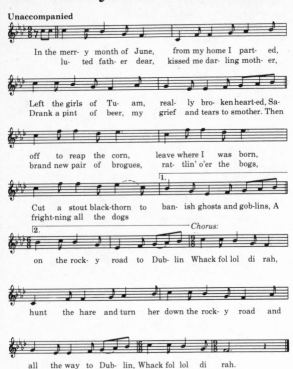

In the merr- y month of June, from my home I part- ed,
lu- ted fath- er dear, kissed me dar- ling moth- er,

Left the girls of Tu- am, real- ly bro- ken heart-ed, Sa-
Drank a pint of beer, my grief and tears to smother. Then

off to reap the corn, leave where I was born,
brand new pair of brogues, rat- tlin' o'er the bogs,

1.
Cut a stout black-thorn to ban- ish ghosts and gob-lins, A
fright-ning all the dogs

2. Chorus:
on the rock- y road to Dub- lin Whack fol lol di rah,

hunt the hare and turn her down the rock- y road and

all the way to Dub- lin, Whack fol lol di rah.

In Mullingar that night I rested limbs so weary,
Started by daylight next mornin' light and airy,
Took a drop of the pure, to keep my heart from sinkin',
That's an Irishman's cure, whene'er he's on for drinking.
To see the lassies smile, laughing all the while,
At my curious style, 'twould set your heart a-bubblin'.
They axed if I was hired, the wages I required,
Till I was almost tired of the rocky road to Dublin.

Chorus

In Dublin next arrived, I thought it such a pity,
To be so soon deprived a view of that fine city.
Then I took a stroll all among the quality,
My bundle it was stole in a neat locality;
Something crossed my mind, then I looked behind,
No bundle could I find upon my stick a wobblin',
Enquirin' for the rogue, they said my Connaught brogue,
Wasn't much in vogue on the rocky road to Dublin.

Chorus

From there I got away, my spirits never failin',
Landed on the quay as the ship was sailin';
Captain at me roared, said that no room had he,
When I jumped aboard, a cabin found for Paddy,
Down among the pigs; I played some funny rigs,
Danced some hearty jigs, the water round me bubblin',
When off Holyhead I wished myself was dead,
Or better far instead, on the rocky road to Dublin.

Chorus

The boys of Liverpool, when we safely landed,
Called myself a fool, I could no longer stand it;
Blood began to boil, temper I was losin',
Poor ould Erin's isle they began abusin'.
'Hurrah my soul,' sez I, my shillelagh I let fly;
Some Galway boys were by, saw I was a-hobblin,
Then with a loud hurray, they joined in the affray.
We quickly cleared the way, for the rocky road to Dublin.

Chorus

The Wind that Shakes the Barley

The lyrics included here to this well-known tune are by Robert Dwyer Joyce.

I sat me in the val- ley green, I
sat me with- my true love- My sad heart strove the
two be- tween, The old love and- the new love- The
old for her, and new that made Me think on Ire- land
dear- ly- While soft the wind blew
down the glen, And shook the gol- den bar- ley

'Twas hard the woeful words to frame
To break the ties that bound us;
But harder still to bear the shame
Of foreign chains around us.
And so I said, 'The mountain glen
I'll seek at morning early,
And join the brave United Men'
While the soft winds shook the barley.

While sad I kissed away her tears
My fond arms round her flinging,
The foeman's shot burst on our ears,
From out the wildwood ringing;
The bullet pierced my true love's side,
In life's young spring so early,
And on my breast in blood she died,
When the soft winds shook the barley.

But blood for blood without remorse
I've ta'en at Oulart Hollow;
I've placed my true love's clay-cold corpse
Where I full soon will follow;
And round her grave I wander drear,
Noon, night and morning early,
With breaking heart whene'er I hear
The wind that shakes the barley.

Dan O'Hara

Well- here I am to- day For God
Chorus: A- chus- la geal mo chree, Won't you

gave and took a- way- And he left without a
buy a box from me- And you'll have the prayers of

home poor Dan O'- Ha- ra.- With my
Dan from Con- ne- ma- ra.- Oh I

match- es in my hand In the frost and snow I
sell them cheap and low- Buy a box be- fore you

stand, And- it's here I am to- ed
go From- your bro- ken heart- ed

day your bro- ken heart- ed.
farm- er Dan- O' Ha- ra.

In the year of sixty-four
I had acres by the score
And the grandest land you ever ran a plough through
But the landlord came you know
And he laid our old home low,
So it's here I am today your broken-hearted.

Chorus

For twenty years or more
Did misfortune cross our door
And my poor old wife and I were sadly parted.
We were scattered far and wide
And our children starved and died,
So it's here I am today your broken-hearted.

Chorus

Tho' in frost and snow I stand
Sure the shadow of God's hand,
It lies warm about the brow of Dan O'Hara,
And soon with God above
I will meet the ones I love,
And I'll find the joys I lost in Connemara.

Chorus

The Rocks of Baun

Come all you loyal heroes wherever you may be, And don't hire with any master 'til you know what your work will be, For you must rise up early in the clear daylight of dawn. And I know you'll never be able to plough the Rocks of Baun.

My shoes are very worn and my stockings they are thin,
My heart is always trembling now for fear they might give in.
My heart is always trembling now from clear daylight 'til dawn,
And I never will be able to plough the Rocks of Baun.

The farmer:

My curse upon you, Sweeney, boy, you have me nearly robbed;
You're sitting by the fireside with your feet upon the hob.
You're sitting by the fireside now from clear daylight 'til dawn
And you never will be able to plough the Rocks of Baun.

Oh, rise up, gallant Sweeney, and get your horse its hay,
And give him a good feed of oats before you start away,
Don't feed him on soft turnip sprigs that grow on yon green lawn,
Or he never will be able to plough the Rocks of Baun.

The worker:

I wish some sergeant-major would send for me in time,
And place me in some regiment all in my youth and prime,
I'd fight for Ireland's glory from the clear daylight 'til dawn
And I never would return again to plough the Rocks of Baun.

Fiddler's Green

Capo 2nd

As I walked by the dock-yard one eve-ning so fair-
To view the salt-wat-er and take the night-air-
I heard an old fish-er-man sing-ing a song-
Oh -take me a-way boys, me time is not long-

Chorus:
Wrap me up in me oil-skins and jum-per-
No more on the docks I'll be seen-
Just tell me old ship-mates I'm tak-ing a trip mates,
And I'll see you some day on Fi-ddl-er's Green-

Now Fiddler's Green is a place I've heard tell,
Where the fishermen go if they don't go to hell,
Where the skies are all clear and the dolphin do play,
And the cold coast of Greenland is far far away.

Chorus

Where the skies are all clear and there's never a gale,
And the fish jump on board with one swish of their tail,
Where you lie at your leisure there's no work to do,
And the skipper's below making tea for the crew.

Chorus

When you get back on the docks and the long trip is through,
There's pubs and there's clubs and there's lassies there too,
Where the girls are all pretty and the beer it is free,
And there's bottles of rum growing from every tree.

Chorus

Now I don't want a harp nor a halo, not me,
Just give a breeze on a good rolling sea,
I'll play me old squeeze box as we sail along,
With the wind in the rigging to sing me a song.

Chorus

Words and music by John Conolly,
copyright 1968 March Music, used by
permission.

The Water Supply

Eddie Callaghan has been writing his own songs, and singing them in the lighthouse in Fanad, Co. Donegal, for many years. I am indebted to him for permission to reproduce *The Water Supply*, and to Patricia Carr.

Unaccompanied

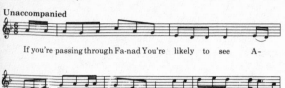

If you're passing through Fa-nad You're likely to see A-

gang of young navvies working hard on the lea. If you ask what they're do-ing they

proud-ly re-ply, 'We-'re working for the council on the wa-ter su-pply.'

No more will the housewife have cause to complain,
If the water runs dry in the well or the drain,
The drains may stop flowing, the wells may run dry,
She can turn on her tap for her water supply.

The farmer of Fanad who works in the clay,
He can now have a bath at the end of the day,
He can go out at night in his collar and tie,
He'll be thankful to God for the water supply.

For the lady going dancing the bath's her delight,
She can scrub till her body is whiter than white,
She can put on her perfume, her powder and dye,
It's a blessing for women this water supply.

It's a boon to the parish the old people say,
Sure it's good for the kidneys and it makes better tay,
There's a spring in their step and a gleam in their eye,
And they talk about nothing but the water supply.

If you're here on a visit and you don't feel so good,
Or your tummy's upset by the rich Fanad food,
There's no need to run to the wee place nearby,
There's an inside convenience with the water supply.

Just step to the bathroom, take a seat on the pot,
No need for a penny to insert in the slot,
Get rid of your worries, just bid them goodbye,
You can flush them away with the water supply.

How did our forefathers live through it all,
They went out in all weathers to answer the call,
They sat on their hunkers and gazed at the sky,
And the least of their thoughts was a water supply.

But those were the days that our forefathers knew,
When hardships were plenty and pleasures were few,
When the nettle and the thistle caused many a sigh,
And they did not have toilets or a water supply.

The pot with the handle is now an antique,
What a tale it could tell if it only could speak,
It was under the bed if a crisis was nigh,
It's redundant, replaced by the water supply.

They talk about astronauts reaching the moon,
They say we'll be having excursions there soon,
But won't it be awkward up there in the sky,
If they don't have a toilet or a water supply.

© Eddie Callaghan

Toe Tapper

'I first heard this tongue twister at Grace Neill's in Donaghadee, Co. Down, where it was sung unaccompanied.

Unaccompanied

Touch her on the toe, that's my chere,
That's my toe-a-tap-per, You can play there. Toe-a- tapper

of my dear, The more I love her I'll ne-ver draw near.

Touch her on the knee, that's my chere,
That's my knee-a-knocker you can play there,
Knee-a-knocker, toe-a-tapper of my dear
The more I love her I'll never draw near.

Touch her on the thigh, that's my chere,
That's my thigh-a-thacker you can play there,
Thigh-a-thacker, knee-a-knocker, toe-a-tapper of my dear
The more I love her I'll never draw near.

Touch her on the navel, that's my chere,
That's my navel-stringer you can play there,
Navel-stringer, thigh-a-thacker, knee-a-knocker, toe-a-tapper of
  my dear
The more I love her I'll never draw near.

Touch her on the breast, that's my chere,
That's my breast-plate you can play there,
Breast-plate, navel-stringer, thigh-a-thacker, knee-a-knocker, toe-
  a-tapper of my dear
The more I love her I'll never draw near.

Touch her on the chin, that's my chere,
That's my chinny-chin you can play there,
Chinny-chin, breast-plate, navel-stringer, thigh-a-thacker, knee-a-
  knocker, toe-a-tapper of my dear
The more I love her I'll never draw near.

Touch her on the mouth, that's my chere,
That's my chatter-box, you can play there,
Chatter-box, chinny-chin, breast-plate, navel-stringer, thigh-a-
  thacker, knee-a-knocker, toe-a-tapper of my dear
The more I love her I'll never draw near.

Touch her on the nose, that's my chere,
That's my snatter-box, you can play there,
Snatter-box, chatter-box, chinny-chin, breast-plate, navel-stringer,
   thigh-a-thacker, knee-a-knocker, toe-a-tapper of my dear
The more I love her I'll never draw near.

Touch her on the eyes, that's my chere,
That's my lookers-at you can play there,
Lookers-at, snatter-box, chatter-box, chinny-chin, breast-plate,
   navel-stringer, thigh-a-thacker, knee-a-knocker, toe-a-tapper of
   my dear
The more I love her I'll never draw near.

Touch her on the head, that's my chere,
That's my louse-trap, you can play there,
Louse-trap, lookers-at, snatter-box, chatter-box, chinny-chin,
   breast-plate, navel-stringer, thigh-a-thacker, knee-a-knocker,
   toe-a-tapper of my dear
The more I love her I'll never draw near.

Blackwater side

Probably the river Blackwater in Co. Cork, this fine air calls for a wide vocal range. (a) Verses 1, 2 & 4. Note that verses 3 and 5 are sung to a slightly different variation (b)

Capo 3rd

(a) One eve- ning fair as I took- the air- Down by Black-wa- ter side- 'Twas gaz- ing- all a- round- me an I- rish- girl I spied

(b) That's not the prom- ise that you gave to- me As you lay u- pon my- breast; You could make- me be-lieve with your ly- ing tongue, The sun rose in the west-

All in the fore part of the night
They rolled in sport and play,
Then the young man arose and he put on his clothes,
Saying, 'Fare thee well today.'

'Go home, go home, to your father's garden,
Go home and cry your fill;
And think of the sad misfortune
brought on with my wanton will.'

36

'There's not a flower in this whole world
As easily led as I;
And when fishes do fly and seas do run dry,
It is then that you'll marry I.'

Pretty Susan, The Pride of Kildare

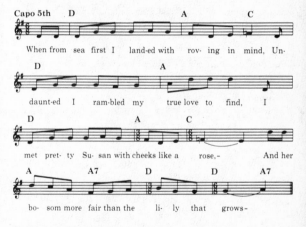

When from sea first I land-ed with rov-ing in mind, Un-
daunt-ed I ram-bled my true love to find, I
met pret-ty Su-san with cheeks like a rose,- And her
bo-som more fair than the li-ly that grows-

Her keen eyes did glitter like bright stars by night,
And the robes she was wearing were costly and white,
Her bare neck was shaded with her long raven hair,
And they call her pretty Susan, the pride of Kildare.

Sometimes I am jovial, sometimes I am sad,
Since my love she is courted by some other lad,
But since we're at a distance, no more I'll despair,
So my blessings on Susan, the pride of Kildare.

The Galway Shawl

In Ar-   ran-   more-
         dia- monds-
In the coun-ty   no   cost- ly

Gal-way -
per- fume-
One plea-, sant   eve-   ning-er
-No paint   or   pow-   der-

in the month of   May-
no-   none at   all-
I   spied   a
She wore   a

col- leen-
bon- net-
she was fair   and   handsome-
with   ri- bbons on it-

her beau-   ty   fair-   took-
And round   her   shoul-   ders-
my-   breath a-
a-   Gal   way

1. G
way-
Chorus: D
She wore   no   shawl-
2. G

As we kept on walking she kept on talking
Till her father's cottage came into view,
Said she, 'Come in, sir, and meet my father,
And for to please him play the "Foggy Dew".'

Chorus

I played the 'Blackbird' and the 'Stack of Barley',
'Rodney's Glory' and the 'Foggy Dew',
She sang each note like an Irish linnet
And the tears flowed in her eyes of blue.

Chorus

'Twas early, early, all in the morning
I hit the road for old Donegal,
Said she, 'Goodbye, sir,' as she cried
And my heart remained with the Galway shawl.

Chorus

© Appletree Press 1983

Reynard the Fox

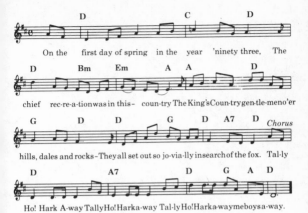

On the first day of spring in the year 'ninety three, The chief rec-re-a-tion was in this- coun-try The King's Coun-try gen-tle-men o'er hills, dales and rocks – They all set out so jo-via-lly in search of the fox. Tal-ly Ho! Hark A-way Tally Ho! Harka-way Tal-ly Ho! Harka-way me boys a-way.

When Reynard was sighted he faced Tobermore,
Arklow and Wicklow along the sea-shore,
They kept his brush in view every yard of the way,
And then he ran his horse right over to Bray.

Chorus

But Reynard, sly Reynard, they hid there that night,
And they swore that they'd watch him until the day-light,
And early next morning the hills did resound,
To the echo of the horn and the cry of the hound.

Chorus

When Reynard was taken his wishes to fulfil,
He sent for ink and paper and a pen to write his will,
And that there that was written, oh, it was no blank,
For he'd left them all a cheque on the National Bank.

Chorus

To you, Johnny Green, I will leave my whole estate,
And to you, Michael Farrell, my money and my plate,
To you, Dan Clancy, my whip, spurs and cap,
For you rode right in front and never looked for the gap.

Chorus

Three Score and Ten

Capo 2nd

Oh! me-thinks I see a host of craft spread-ing their sails a-lee, As down the Hum ber they do-glide bound for the Northern Sea,- Me-thinks I see on each small craft a host of hearts so brave, Go-ing out to earn their dai-ly bread up-on the rest-less waves. And it's three score and

Chorus:

ten, boys and men were lost from Grims-by Town, From Yar-mouth down to Scar-bor-ough many hundreds more were drowned. Our herr-ing craft, our trawl-ers, our fishing smacks as well, They-'ve gone to fight that bit-ter night and bat-tle with the swell

Oh! methinks I see them yet again as they leave this land behind,
Casting their nets into the sea, their herring shoals to find,
Methinks I see them yet again and then no more do ride,
With their nets go sweep and their decks cleared up and their side
    lights burning bright.

Chorus

Now October's night brought such a sight it was never seen before,
There were masts and yards and broken spars washed up upon the
    shore,

40

There was many's a heart of sorrow there was many's a heart so
   brave,
There was many's a fine and healthy lad to find a watery grave.

Chorus

The Mermaid

It was Friday morn when we set sail and we were not far from the land— Our Captain he spied a mermaid so fair With a comb and a glass in her hand. And the ocean waves do roll— And the stormy winds do blow— And we poor sailor boys were sitting up aloft while the landlubbers lay down below, below, below While the landlubbers lay down below

Then up spoke the Captain of our gallant ship,
And a fine spoken man was he,
This fishy mermaid has warned me of our doom,
We shall sink to the bottom of the sea.

Chorus

Then up spoke the mate of our gallant ship,
And a grand old fellow was he,
Saying I have a wife in Salem by the sea,
And tonight a widow she will be.

Chorus

Then up spoke the cabin boy of our gallant ship,
And a cheeky young laddie was he,
Saying I have a girlfriend in Brooklyn by the sea
And tonight she'll be weeping for me.

Chorus

Then up spoke the cook of our gallant ship,
And a bloody old butcher was he,
Saying I care no more for my pots and my pans
They shall sink to the bottom of the sea.

Chorus

Three times around spun our gallant ship,
And three times around spun she,
Three times around spun our gallant ship,
And she sank to the bottom of the sea.

Chorus

Finnegan's Wake

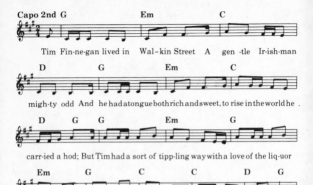

Capo 2nd

Tim Fin-ne-gan lived in Wal-kin Street A gen-tle Ir-ish-man migh-ty odd And he had a tongue both rich and sweet, to rise in the world he carried a hod; But Tim had a sort of tipp-ling way with a love of the liq-uor Tim was born to send him on his way each day he'd a drop of cray-thur every morn.

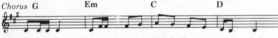

Chorus

Whack fol the dah, dance to your part-ner Welt the flure yer trot-ters shake,

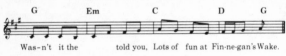

Was-n't it the truth I told you, Lots of fun at Fin-ne-gan's Wake.

One morning Tim felt rather full,
His head felt heavy which made him shake,
He fell from the ladder and broke his skull,
So they carried him home his corpse to wake,
They rolled him up in a nice clean sheet,
And laid him out upon the bed,
With a gallon of whiskey at his feet,
And a barrel of porter at his head.
Chorus
His friends assembled at the wake,
And Mrs. Finnegan called for lunch,
First they brought in tay and cake,
Then pipes, tobacco, and whiskey punch.
Miss Biddy O'Brien began to cry,
'Such a neat, clean corpse did you ever see,
Arrah, Tim avourneen, why did you die?'
'Ah, hould your bag,' said Paddy M'Gee.
Chorus
Then Biddy O'Connor took up the job,
'Biddy,' says she, 'you're wrong I'm sure,'
But Biddy gave her a belt on the gob,
And left her sprawling on the floor.

Oh, then war did soon enrage;
'Twas woman to woman and man to man,
Shillelagh law did all engage,
And a row and a ruction soon began.

Chorus

Then Mickey Maloney raised his head,
When a noggin of whiskey flew at him,
It missed and falling on the bed,
The liquor scattered over Tim;
Bedad, he revives, see how he rises,
And Timothy rising from the bed,
Says, 'Whirl your liquor round like blazes,
Thunderin' Jasus, do you think I'm dead?'

Chorus

Paddy Lie Back

On a cold and mist-y morn-ing in Sep- tem- ber With all of me mon- ey be- ing spent, Where it went to oh– Lord I don't re- mem- ber– So a- round to the ship-ping of- fice I went

Chorus:

Oh Pad-dy lie back, Oh Pad-dy lie back; take in your slack, take in your slack, Take a han- dle of the cap- stan, haul a- way; Oh we're bound to sail for Eng-land boys be han- dy– And we're bound for Val- pa- rai- so in the morn.

Last night there was a helluva crowd of sailors,
For the colonies, for 'Frisco and for France;
And I slipped aboard a lively barque, the Hotspur,
And I was paralytic drunk at the very first chance.

Chorus

There were Germans, there were Poles and there were Russians,
There was jolly Jack just come across from France,
And not one of them could speak a word of English,
But if you played a tune they'd all get up and dance.

Chorus

I wakened in the morning sick and sore,
I wished I'd never gone to sea again,
When a voice came thundering down through the floor,
'On deck and pay attention to your name'.

Chorus

Well I wish that I was safely in the boozer,
With Kitty or with Maggie on my knee,
And I know exactly what I'd like to do now,
And if you were there you'd do the same as me.

Chorus

Follow Me Up To Carlow

This heady song was written by P. J. McCall about the battle of
Glenmalure in 1580.

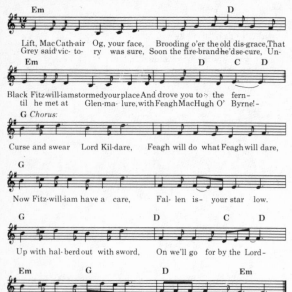

Lift, MacCath-air Og, your face, Brooding o'er the old dis-grace, That
Black Fitz-will-iam stormed your place And drove you to the fern-

Grey said vic-to-ry was sure, Soon the fire-brand he'd se-cure, Until he met at Glen-ma-lure, with Feagh MacHugh O' Byrne! -

G Chorus:

Curse and swear Lord Kil-dare, Feagh will do what Feagh will dare,

Now Fitz-will-iam have a care, Fal-len is- your star low.

Up with hal-berd out with sword, On we'll go for by the Lord-

Feagh MacHugh has giv-en the word, 'Foll-ow me up to Car-low'.

See the swords of Glen Imail
Flashing o'er the English Pale,
See the children of the Gael
Beneath O'Byrne's banners.
Rooster of a fighting stock,
Would you let a Saxon cock
Crow out upon an Irish rock;
Fly up and teach him manners.

Chorus

From Tassagart to Clonmore
Flows a stream of Saxon gore,
Och! great was Ruari Og O'More
At sending loons to Hades.
White is sick and Lane is fled—
Now for black Fitzwilliam's head—
We'll send it over dripping red
To Liza and her ladies.

Chorus

The Molly Maguires

Capo 4th

Ch: Make way for the Molly Maguires They're liars they're drinkers, but they're men. Make way for the Molly Maguires You'll never see the likes of them again. Down the mine no diamonds shine, The pit as black as hell— In mud and slime they do their time In Paddy's prison cell— And they cursed the day that they sailed away, And drowned their sorrows in a jar

Chorus

Backs may break and muscles ache
Down there's no time to dream,
Of fields and farms and a woman's arms,
It's dig that bloody seam;
Though they break their bodies underground
None dare to push them around.

49

The Boys of Killybegs

There are wild and rock-y hills on the coast of Do- ne- gal And the
fish- er- men are hard-y, brave and free— And the
big At- lan- tic swell is a place they know right well As they
fight to take a liv-ing from the sea— With a

Chorus:

pleas-ant roll-ing sea, and the herr-ing runn-ing free, The
fleet all rid- ing gent-ly through the foam— When the
boats are load- ed down, there'll be sing-ing in the town, When the
boys of Kill- y- begs come roll- ing home.

Now you've donned your rubber boots, and you've got your oilskins
on,
And you've checked your gear to see it's all O.K.
And your jumper keeps you warm, for it's cold before the dawn,
And you're ready to begin another day.

Chorus

Now you're headed out to sea and the wind is blowing free
And you cast your nets as rain begins to fall
But the sun comes riding high and the clouds will soon roll by
And today you'll maybe get a bumper haul.

Chorus

Now there's purple on the hills and there's green down on the shore
And the sun has spilled its gold upon the sea
And there's silver down below, where the herring fishes go,
When we catch them there'll be gold for you and me.

Chorus

Now the weather's growing rough and the work is plenty tough
And the ropes will raise the welts upon your hands
But you'll never leave the sea, for whoever you may be
When it's in your blood, it's hard to live on land.

Chorus

Carrickfergus

I wish I was- in Carr-ick- fer- gus-

On- ly for nights- in Ball-y- gran-

I would swim over- the deep-est o- cean-

on- ly for nights- in Ball-y- gran-

But the sea is wide- and I cannot swim o- ver-

And neith-er have- I- the wings to fly-

I wish I could find- a hand-some boat - man-

To ferry me o- ver- to my love and die.

My boyhood days bring back sad reflections
Of happy hours I spent so long ago,
Of boyhood friends and my own relations
Are all passed on now, like drifting snow;
But I'll spend my days an endless rover,
Soft is the grass I walk, my bed is free;
Ah, to be back in Carrickfergus
On that long road, down to the sea.

But in Kilkenny it is reported
There are marble stones there, as black as ink,
With gold and silver I would support her
But I'll sing no more now till I get a drink.

I'm drunk today and I'm seldom sober,
A handsome rover from town to town,
Ah, but I'm sick now and my days are numbered
So come all you young men and lay me down.

The Banks of the Roses

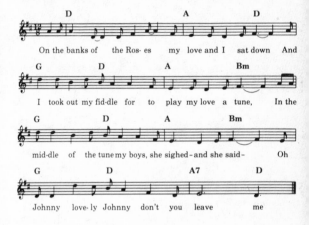

On the banks of the Ros-es my love and I sat down And
I took out my fid-dle for to play my love a tune, In the
mid-dle of the tune my boys, she sighed–and she said– Oh
Johnny love-ly Johnny don't you leave me

When I was a young man I heard my father say
That he'd rather see me dead and buried in the clay,
Sooner than be married to any runaway,
By the lovely sweet banks of the roses.

And then I am no runaway and soon I'll let them know
That I can take the bottle or can leave it alone,
And if her daddy doesn't like it, he can keep his daughter at home,
And young Johnny will go roving with another.

And when I get married 'twill be in the month of May,
When the leaves they are green and the meadows they are gay,
And me and my true love we'll sit and sport and play,
By the lovely sweet banks of the roses.

The Jug of Punch

'Twas ver-y early in the month of June As-
I was sit-ting- in my room- A small bird sang on an
i- vy bush And the song she sang was the Jug of Punch Too-ral
loo-ral lay Too-ral loo-ral lay Too-ral loo-ral lay Too-ral
loo-ral lay A small bird sang on an
i- vy bush and the song she sang was the. Jug of Punch

What more diversion can a man desire,
Than to be seated by a snug coal fire,
Upon his knee a pretty wench,
And on the table a jug of punch.

Now when I am dead and in my grave,
No costly tombstone will I crave
Just lay me down in my native heath
With a jug of punch at my head and feet.

The Jolly Beggar

It's of a Jol-ly Beg-gar-man came trip-ping o'er the
plain— He came un-to a farm-er's door a
lodg-ing for to gain— The
rov- ing a rov-ing in the night— We'll
go no more a- rov-ing let the moon- shine so
bright- We'll go no more a- rov- ing.

far-mer's daughter she came down and viewed him cheek and
chin- She said he is a hand-some man, I
pray you take him in— *Chorus:* We'll go no more a-

He would not lie within the barn nor yet within the byer,
But he would in the corner lie, down by the kitchen fire,
And when the Beggar's bed was made of good clean sheets and hay,
Down beside the kitchen fire the Jolly Beggar lay.

Chorus

The farmer's daughter she came down to bolt the kitchen door,
And there she saw the Beggar standing naked on the floor.
He took the daughter in his arms and to the bed he ran
Kind sir, she says, be easy now, you'll waken our good man.

Chorus

Now you are no beggar, you are some gentleman,
For you have stole my maidenhead and I am quite undone.
I am no Lord, I am no Squire, of beggars I be one,
And beggars they be robbers all, so you are quite undone.

Chorus

She took the bed in both her hands and threw it at the wall,
Saying, go you with the Beggarman, my maidenhead and all.
We'll go no more a roving, a roving in the night,
We'll go no more a roving, let the moon shine so bright,
We'll go no more a roving.

The Holy Ground

The waterfront at Cobh, Co. Cork, is reputed to be the 'Holy Ground' of the title. Some claim that the song hails from Swansea in Wales, others that it originated in New York!

Fare- well my love- ly- Di- nah, A thou- sand times- A- dieu- For we're go- ing a- way from the Ho- ly Ground, And the girls we all- loved true- We'll- sail the South- Seas o- ver and- we'll re- turn for sure- To see a- gain the girls we love and the Ho- ly Ground once more- To the girl I do a- dore- And still I live in hope to see the- Ho- ly Ground once more-

Oh, the night was dark and stormy,
You scarce could see the moon,
And our good old ship was tossed about,
And her rigging all was torn:
With her seams agape and leaky,
With her timbers dozed and old,

And still I live in hopes to see,
The Holy Ground once more.
You're the girl I do adore
And still I live in hopes to see,
The Holy Ground once more,
Fine girl you are!

And now the storm is over,
And we are safe on shore,
Let us drink a health to the Holy Ground
And the girls that we adore;
We will drink strong ale and porter
Till we make the tap room roar
And when our money is all spent
We will go to sea once more.
You're the girl I do adore
And still I live in hopes to see
The Holy Ground once more,
Fine girl you are!

Haul Away Joe

A sea shanty, often sung unaccompanied. 'Tammy' is sung very loudly, and 'Heave haul away' is sung by all.

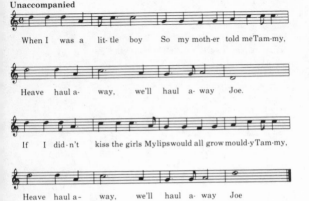

Unaccompanied

When I was a lit-tle boy So my moth-er told me Tam-my,

Heave haul a- way, we'll haul a- way Joe.

If I did-n't kiss the girls My lips would all grow mould-y Tam-my,

Heave haul a- way, we'll haul a- way Joe

Once I knew an English girl
And she was fat and lazy 'Tammy',
Heave haul away, we'll haul away Joe.
Then I met an Irish girl
She damn near drove me crazy 'Tammy',
Heave haul away, we'll haul away Joe.

Kind Louis was the king of France
Before the revolution
Heave haul away, we'll haul away Joe.
Then he got his head cut off
Which spoiled his constitution.
Heave haul away, we'll haul away Joe.

Slieve Gallion Braes

A ballad, gaining recently in popularity, sung unaccompanied and with little ornamentation.

It's oft I did ramble with my dog and my gun,
I roamed through the glens for joy and for fun,
But those days are now all over and I can no longer stay,
So farewell unto ye, bonny, bonny Slieve Gallion braes.

How oft of an evening and the sun in the west,
I roved hand in hand with the one I loved best:
But the hopes of youth are vanished and now I'm far away,
So farewell unto ye, bonny, bonny Slieve Gallion braes.

O! it was not for the want of employment at home,
That caused the young sons of old Ireland to roam,
But the rents are getting higher and I can no longer stay,
So farewell unto ye, bonny, bonny Slieve Gallion braes.

Sailing in the Lowlands Low

Dun- more we quit- ted, Mich-ael-mas gone by,
Cow- hides and wool- and live car- go, Twent-y young
Wild Geese read- y fledged to fly! Sail-ing for the Low-lands
Low– *Chorus:* The Low- lands Low, The Low- lands
Low, Sail-ing in the Low- lands Low–

Sean Paor's the skipper, from the Cobh of Cork—
Piery keeps log for his father!
Crew all from Bannow, Fethard and the Hook—
Sailing in the Lowlands Low!

Chorus

These twenty Wild Geese gave Queen Anne the slip,
Crossing to Lewey in Flanders:
He and Jack Malbrook both are in a grip,
Fighting in the Lowlands Low!

Chorus

Ready with priming we'd our galliot gun:
Muskets and pikes in good order!
We should be riddled—captives would be none!
Death! or else the Lowlands Low!

Chorus

Pray, holy Brendan, Turk or Algerine,
Ditchman nor Saxon may sink us!
We'd bring Geneva, rack and Rhenish wine
Safely from the Lowlands Low!

Chorus

© Appletree Press 1983

I'll Tell Me Ma

Originally a children's song, this, almost standard, 'pub' rendering is now heard as often in Cork as in Belfast, where it was set.

I'll tell me ma when I get home, The boys won't leave the girls a- lone, They pull my hair, they steal my comb, But that's all right when I get home. She is hand-some, she is pret-ty, She is the belle of Bel- fast cit- y, She is a court-ing one, two, three. Please won't you tell me - who is she.

Albert Mooney says he loves her,
All the boys are fighting for her,
They rap at the door and they ring at the bell,
Saying, 'Oh, my true love, are you well?'
Out she comes as white as snow,
Rings on her fingers, bells on her toes,
Old Johnny Murray says she'll die,
If she doesn't get the fellow with the roving eye.

Let the wind and the rain and the hail blow high
And the snow come travelling from the sky,
She's as nice as apple-pie,
And she'll get her own lad bye and bye.
When she gets a lad of her own,
She won't tell her ma when she gets home,
Let them all come as they will,
But it's Albert Mooney she loves still.

The Spanish Lady

As I roved out through Dublin ci-ty-
Who should I see but a Span-ish la-dy-
At the hour of twelve at night Lass-ie I have
Comb-ing her hair by can-dle-light.
come a-court-ing Your kind fav-ours for to win-
And if you'd but smile u-pon me- Sun-day night I'll
call a-gain-

Chorus: Whack fol the too-ral too-ral ad-dy-
Whack fol the too-ral oo-ral ay oo-ral ay.

As I came back through Dublin city
At the hour of half past eight
Whom should I spy but a Spanish lady
Brushing her hair in broad daylight.
First she tossed it then she brushed it,
On her lap was a silver comb;
In all my life I ne'er did see
A maid so fair since I did roam.

Chorus

As I came back through Dublin city
When the sun began to set
Whom should I spy but a Spanish lady
Catching a moth in a golden net.
When she saw me, then she fled me
Lifting her petticoat over her knee,
In all my life I ne'er did see
A maid so blithe as the Spanish lady.

Chorus

Reprinted by permission of the Copyright
Owners
Boosey & Hawkes Music Publishers Ltd.

I'm a Rover

I'm a ro- ver, sel-dom so- ber, I'm a ro- ver of high de-gree – It's when I'm drink-ing I'm al- ways think-ing, How to gain my- love's com- pa- ny. I'm a ny

Though the night be as dark as dungeon,
Not a star to be seen above
I will be guided without a stumble
Into the arms of my own true love.

He stepped up to her bedroom window;
Kneeling gently upon a stone
He rapped at her bedroom window:
'Darling dear, do you lie alone.

'It's only me your own true lover;
Open the door and let me in;
For I have come on a long journey,
And I'm near drenched unto the skin.'

She opened the door with the greatest pleasure,
She opened the door and she let him in;
They both took hands and embraced each other;
Until the morning they lay as one.

The cocks were crowing, the birds were singing,
The burns they ran free about the brae;
'Remember lass I'm a ploughman's laddie,
And the farmer I must obey.

'Now my love I must go and leave thee;
And though the hills they are high above,
I will climb them with greater pleasure,
Since I've been in your arms my love.'

James Connolly

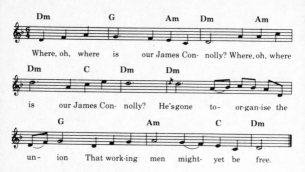

Where, oh, where is our James Con- nolly? Where, oh, where
is our James Con- nolly? He's gone to- or-gan-ise the
un- ion That work-ing men might- yet be free.

Then who, then who will lead the van?
Then who, then who will lead the van?
Who, but our James Connolly
The hero of the working man.

Who will carry high the burning flag?
Who will carry high the burning flag?
Who but our James Connolly,
Could carry high the burning flag.

Oh, they carried him up to the jail,
Oh, they carried him up to the jail,
And they shot him down on a bright May morning
And quickly laid him in his gore.

Who mourns the death of this great man?
Who mourns the death of this great man?
Oh, bury me down in yon green garden,
With union men on every side.

Oh, they buried him down in yon green garden
With union men on every side
And they swore they would form a mighty weapon
That James Connolly's name could be filled with pride.

Where, oh, where is our James Connolly?
Where, oh, where is our James Connolly?
He's gone to organise the union,
That working men, they might yet be free.

The Wild Rover

I've been a wild ro-ver for ma-ny's a year-
And I've spent all my mo-ney on whis-key and beer-
And now I'm re-turn-ing with gold in great store-
And I ne-ver will play the wild ro-ver no more. And it's no! nay! nev-er! *(Clap four times)*
no nay nev-er no more, And I'll play the wild ro-ver- no nev-er- no more.

I went into an alehouse I used to frequent,
And I told the landlady my money was spent.
I asked her for credit, she answered me nay,
Saying custom like yours I can have any day.

Chorus

I took from my pocket ten sovereigns bright,
And the landlady's eyes opened wide with delight,
She said I have whiskeys and wines of the best,
And the words that I told you were only in jest.

Chorus

I'll go home to my parents, confess what I've done
And I'll ask them to pardon their prodigal son.
And when they have kissed me as oft-times before,
I never will play the wild rover no more.

Chorus

Whiskey in the Jar

As I was go- ing o- ver the far famed Ker-ry mountains, I
met with Cap-tain Far-rell and his mo-ney he was count-ing- I
first prod-uced my pis- tol and then put out my rap-ier Saying
stand and de- liv- er for you are the bold de- ceiv-er With my
whack fol the dol fol the da whack fol the dah di oh,
Whack fol the dah de oh There's whis-key in the jar.

He counted out his money and it made a pretty penny,
I put it in my pocket and I gave it to my Jenny,
She sighed and she swore that she never would betray me,
But the devil take the women for they never can be easy.

Chorus

I went unto my chamber all for to take a slumber,
I dreamt of gold and jewels and sure it was no wonder,
But Jenny drew my charges and she filled them up with water,
And she sent for Captain Farrell, to be ready for the slaughter.

Chorus

And 'twas early in the morning before I rose to travel,
Up comes a band of footmen and likewise Captain Farrell;
I then produced my pistol, for she stole away my rapier
But I couldn't shoot the water so a prisoner I was taken.

Chorus

And if anyone can aid me, 'tis my brother in the army,
If I could learn his station in Cork or in Killarney.
And if he'd come and join me we'd go roving in Kilkenny,
I'll engage he'd treat me fairer than my darling sporting Jenny.

Chorus

There's some take delight in the hurling and the bowling,
Others take delight in the carriages a-rolling;
But I take delight in the juice of the barley,
And courting pretty women when the sun is rising early.

Chorus

Don't Call Me Early in the Morning

Written by Tommy Sands, of the Sands family. This songs warns of the dangers of overwork.

Capo 2nd

Chorus: Don't call me ear- ly in the morn- ing
Call me what you want to, but leave me a- lone.
Don't call me ear- ly in the morn- ing, Just
leave me 'till the cows are com- ing home— Well a
man's- a man— but he needs his re- lax-a- tion From
ris- ing al- ways at- the dawn And the
heart of the mat-ter- to- mor- row is a Sa-tur-day And
I'll be ly- in'- on

Chorus

Sad the lad that can't rest contented
He has it all but must have more
He fills himself with pills, to retire with a million
But falls asleep at sixty-four.

Chorus

Fair is fair, and I've done my share
My nerves are getting on my nerves.
If you don't have a pillow with a white swan's feather
I'll do with a corner for my head.

Chorus

Just a gentle warning for tomorrow morning,
No big noises near my room,
Cars with no exhausts, chickens with the whooping cough,
Milkmen that whistle out of tune.

Chorus

The Great Shipyard Protest Parade

My thanks to Arnold Gardiner, the author of this contemporary monologue.

I work down the Queen's Islan'
(The place where the big ships are made)
An' I thought that I'd tell ye the story
Of the Great Shipyard Protest Parade.

I shouldn't work in the shipyard
For I've got plenty of brains
But the 'Brue' got fed up supportin'
Meself, and the wife—and ten weans!

For years I tried to make money
But somehow I just couldn't click—
For the horses kept on runnin' slower
And the Guinness kept on runnin' quick.

But anyway, back to my story,
I was a helper down in the Yard—
But as no-one was doi' a rap there
Helpin' them wasn't too hard.

But although there wasn't much work done,
One thing I saw straight away,
There was always some eejit protestin'
Or with something to say.

There was anti-Vietnam demonstrators
There was them as said 'Bring back the Cat'
And a fella who lived up the Shankill
Who swore that the world was dead flat.

Some said abolish the Border
And drew tri-colours up on the walls
And a Worshipful Master from Bloomfield
Who wanted to blow up the Falls.

Where ever you went there were placards
All hung up with wee bits of rope
Some said 'Celtic for Ever'
And others said 'Paisley for Pope'.

One day there was some of us sittin'
Discussin' the Blues and the Glens
Debatin' the world situation
And boilin' the tea in our kens.

Me and wee Johnson were talkin'
When an idea came into our minds
That we'd organise a procession
Like the Twelfth—but on smaller lines.

We'd invite all the bloomin' protesters
To come and stand up for their views
An' we'd do all of the plannin'
And charge half-a-crown—Walkin' Dues.

We agreed on a route with the Polis
The big sergeant was dacent enough
He said that he'd send down a Peeler
In case anybody got rough.

When the day came, the whole of the Shipyard
Downed tools and turned out to see
The great Protest Demonstration
Planned by wee Johnson—and me.

There was banners of all shapes and sizes
An' flags all gaudy an' bright
An' a bunch of Gospel fanatics
Shoutin' 'The end is in sight'.

There was a couple of oul' bookies runners
In case we'd got money to lose
An' I think there was also a Rabbi
Who came down down to look after the Jews.

We had every known agitator
All determined to have their own say
An' a Black in a Sash an' a turban
Who'd started a Lodge in Bombay.

Wee Johnson had got them all ready—
For he was to lead the march-past,
When a note arrived from his Reverence
Complainin' he hadn't been asked.

Well, at last we got the thing started
Such a sight ye never have seen,
With red, white and blue—and some purple
All mixed up with orange and green.

The route that we'd planned was quite simple
It was down the Queen's Road and back,
Then up the gangway of a tanker
To end with a rally on deck

Wee Johnson was lovin' each minute
His chest was swelled out with pride
Like King Billy, in front of his army—
Except he'd got no horse to ride.

This pride was to prove his undoing
His end was indeed near at hand
For he led them all up the wrong gangway
Not onto the ship we had planned.

Now this ship wasn't quite finished
She'd no rail along the far side
But the eejits were busy protestin'
And marched on—and fell into the tide.

So for once the Prods and the Mickies
Didn't meet up with a clash
For they all fell into the water
With one big ignorant splash.

It's quiet now in the shipyard
There's no-one has got much to say,
But I shed an odd tear for wee Johnson—
And the masterless Lodge in Bombay.

© Arnie Gardiner